# Tranquil
## Dot-to-Dot

# Tranquil
## Dot-to-Dot

ARCTURUS

ARCTURUS

This edition published in 2018 by Arcturus Publishing Limited
26/27 Bickels Yard, 151–153 Bermondsey Street,
London SE1 3HA

ISBN: 978-1-78888-030-5
CH006356NT
Supplier 29, Date 0118, Print run 6781

Printed in China

Created for children 10+

# Introduction

Here you will find a wonderful range of absorbing dot-to-dot puzzles to give you sanctuary from your busy world. Let your brain find a moment of tranquility by focusing on these simple, yet intricate images.

There are more than 150 visual puzzles to get stuck in to. Simply locate the first dot labeled 1 and use a pencil to join it to the next dot and so on, in ascending order. We recommend you use a ruler to trace the lines between each of the dots, but you can also try it freehand if you're on the go. The handy pocket-book size of this book makes it ideal for carrying around with you for whenever the mood strikes.

Every one of these images contains anywhere between 150 and 200 dots, giving you the perfect amount of time to relax your brain and channel your thoughts into new and creative pastures. The subjects range from flowers, animals, and famous settings to spiritual symbols and zodiac constellations, so there is plenty of variety to keep you guessing.

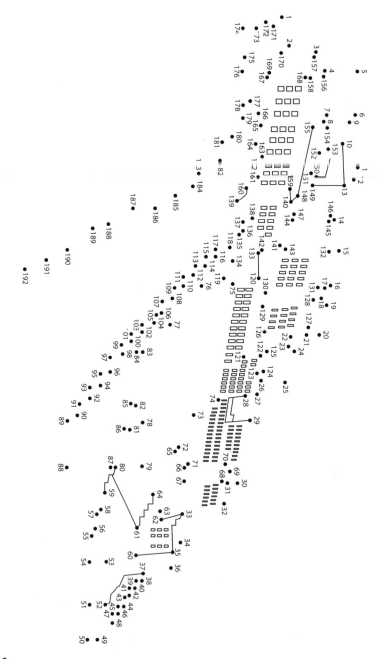

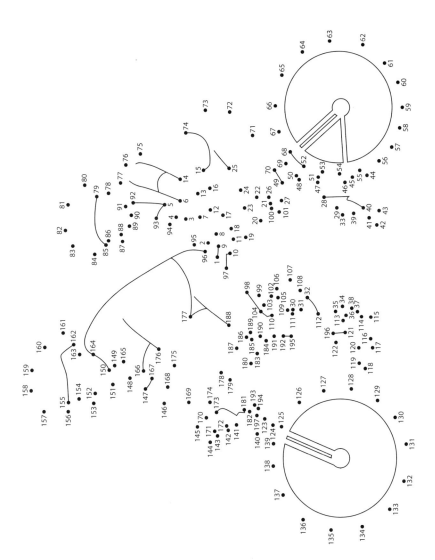

7

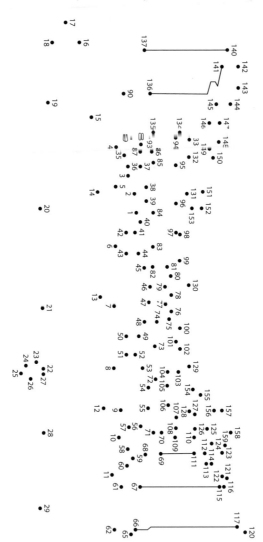

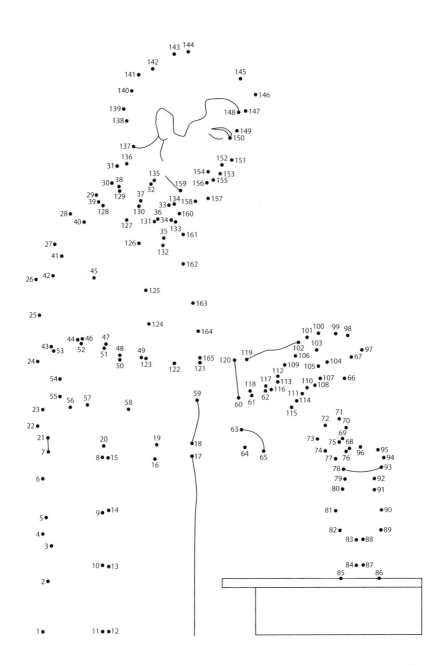

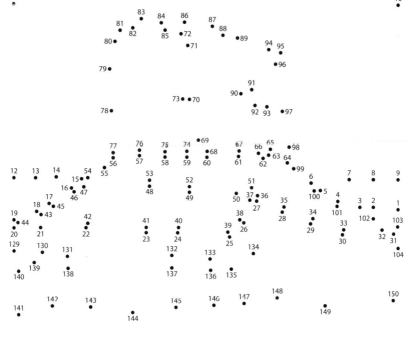
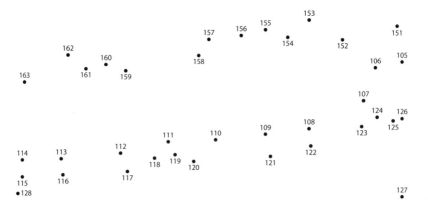

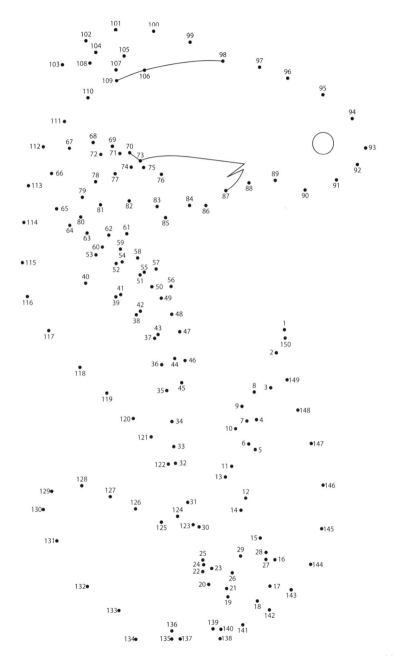

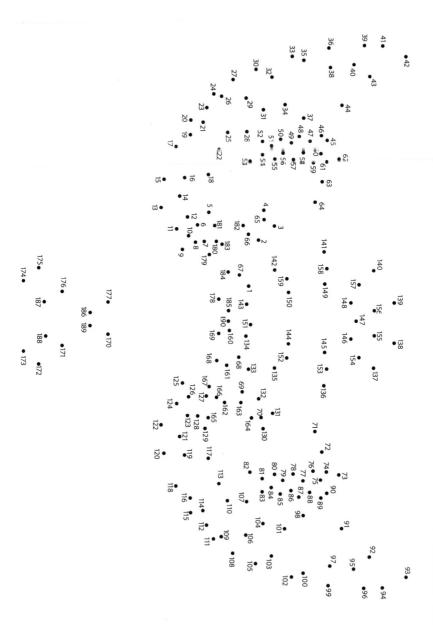

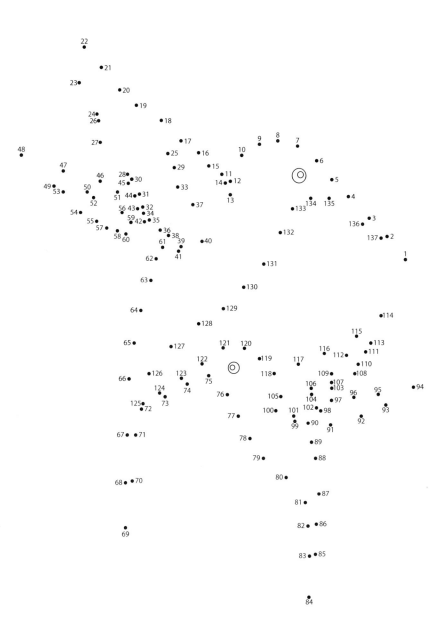

13

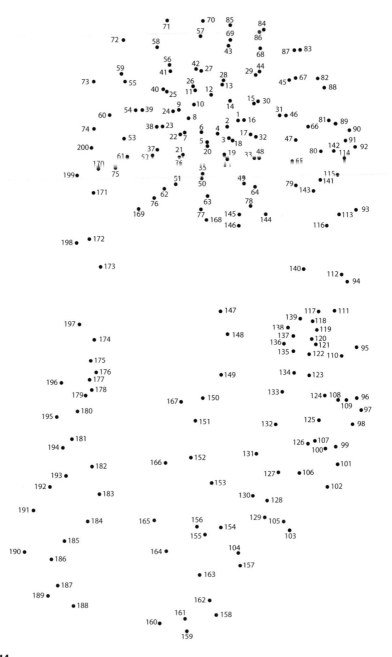

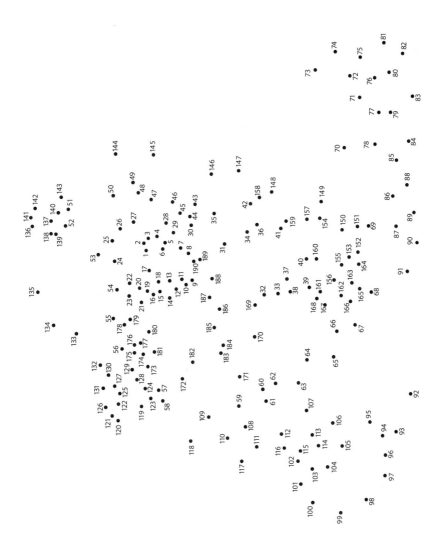

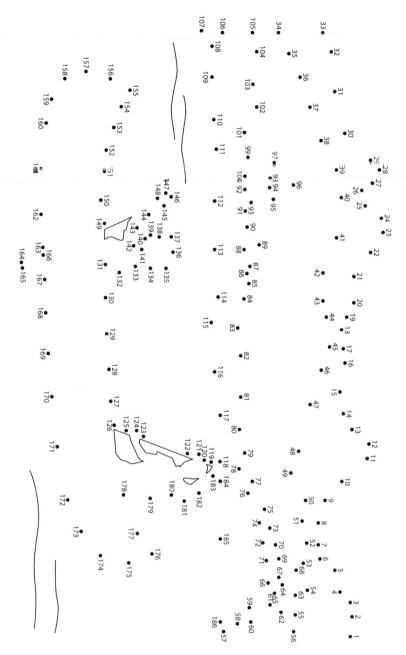

17

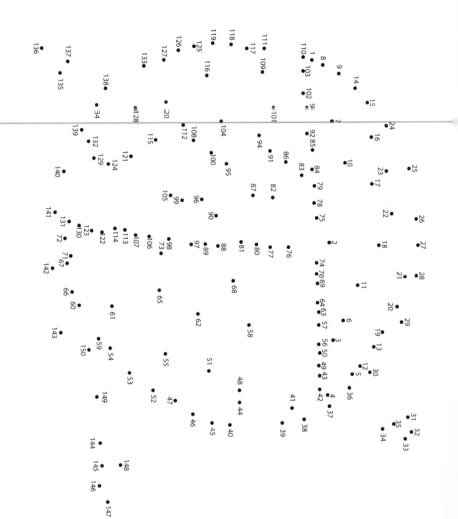

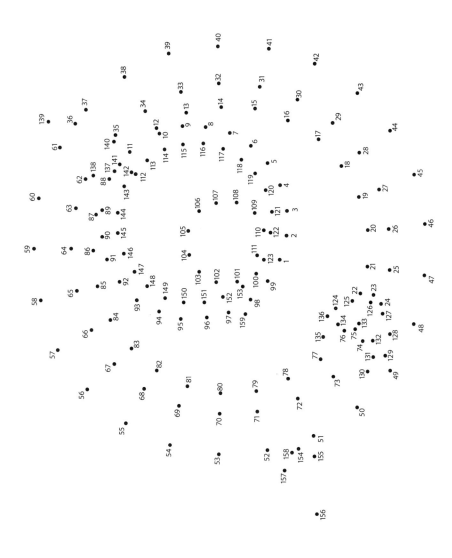

19

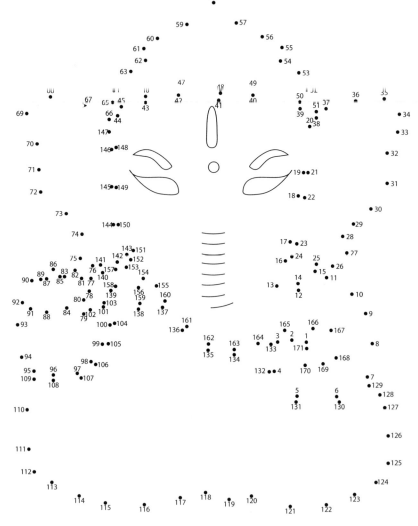

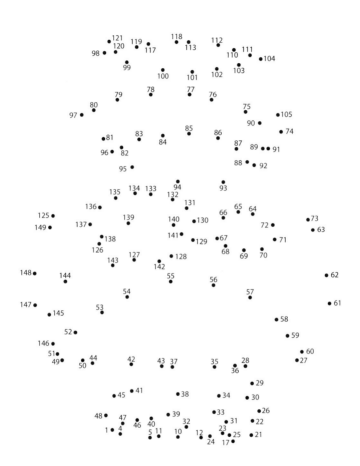

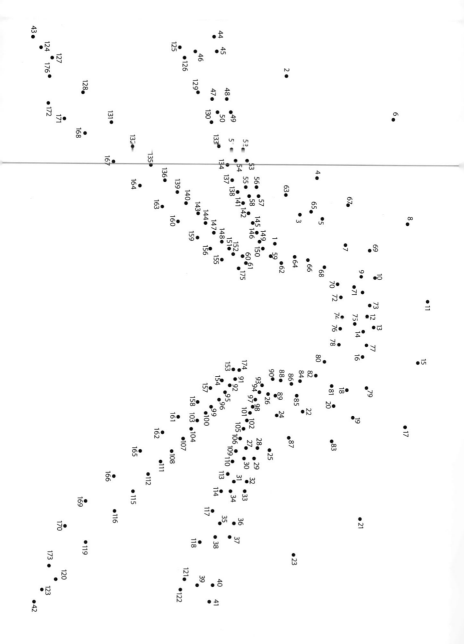

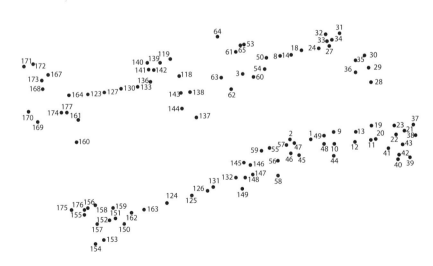

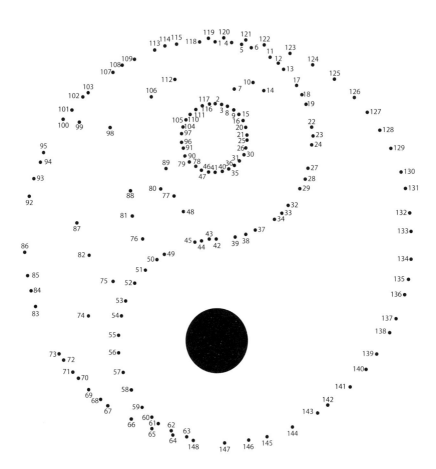

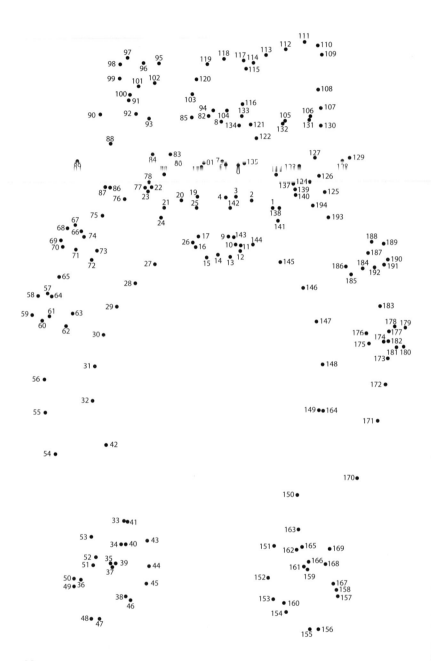

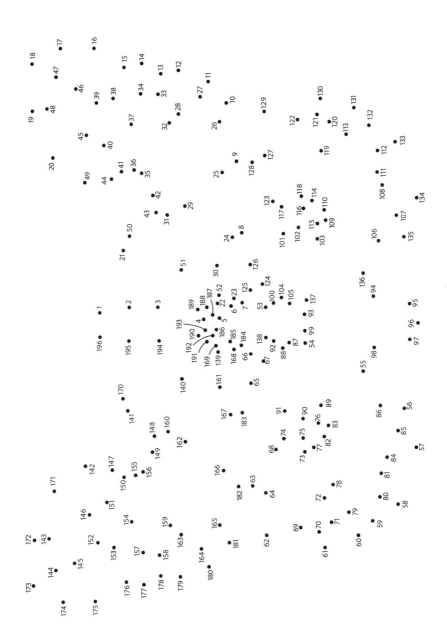

27

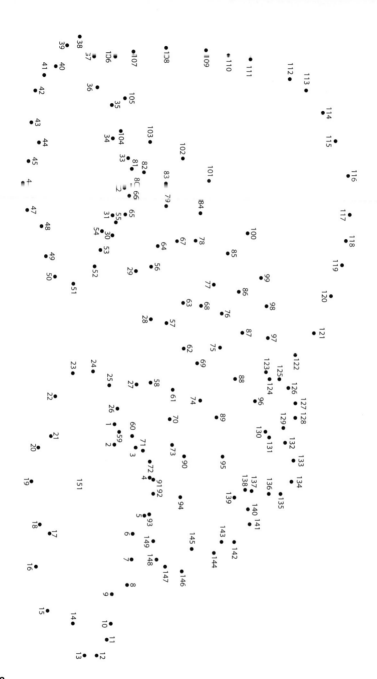

28

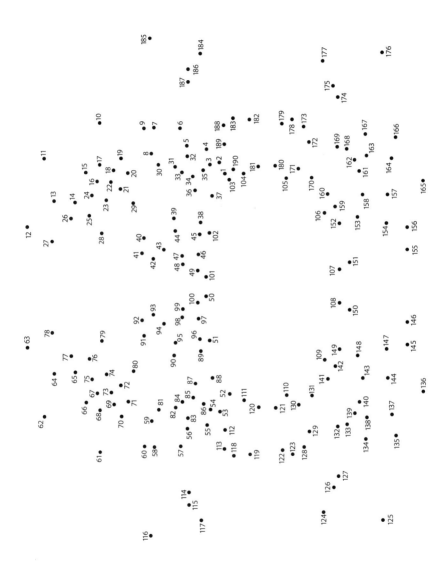

29

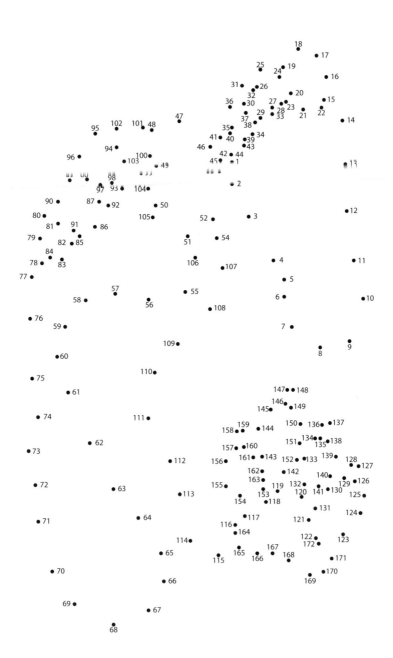

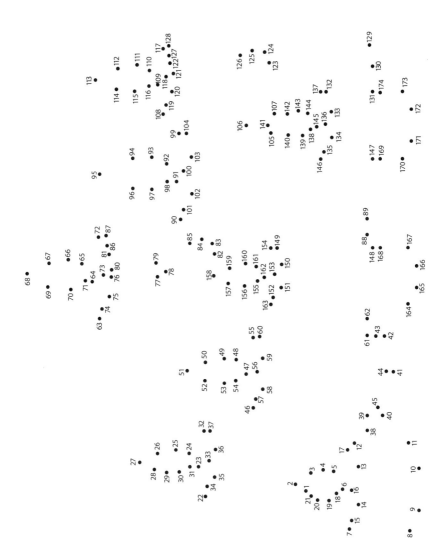

31

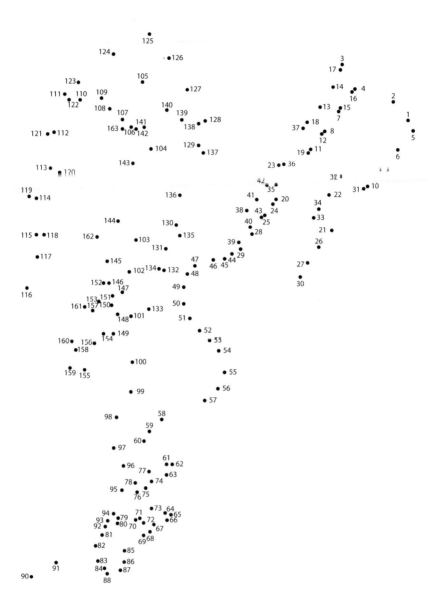

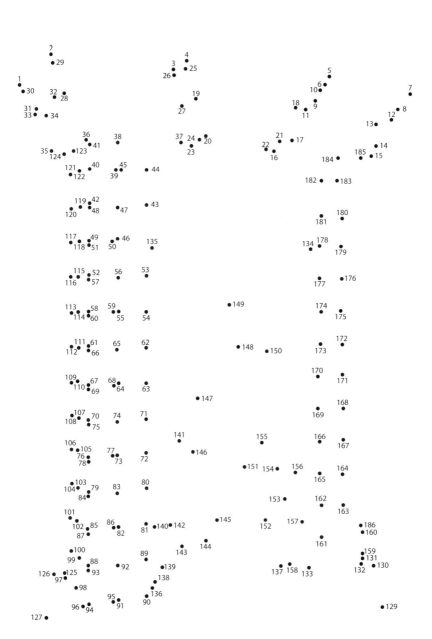

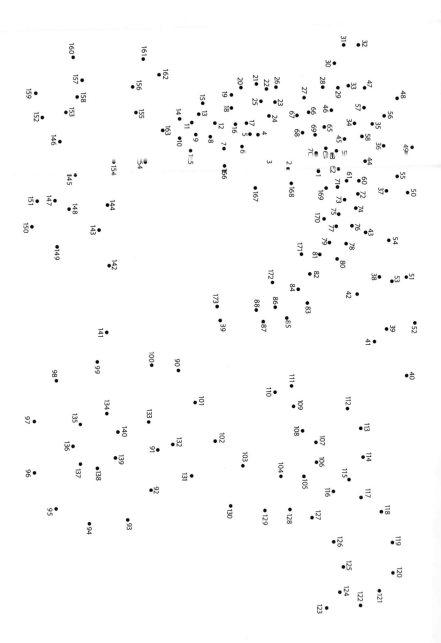

34

35

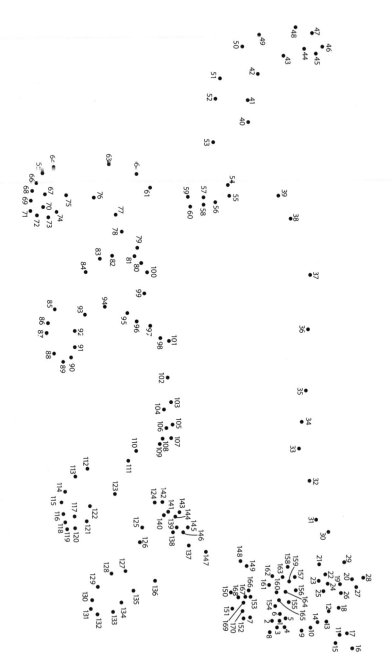

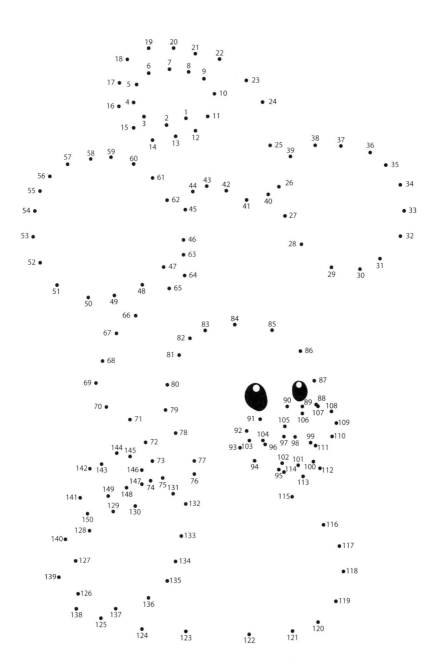

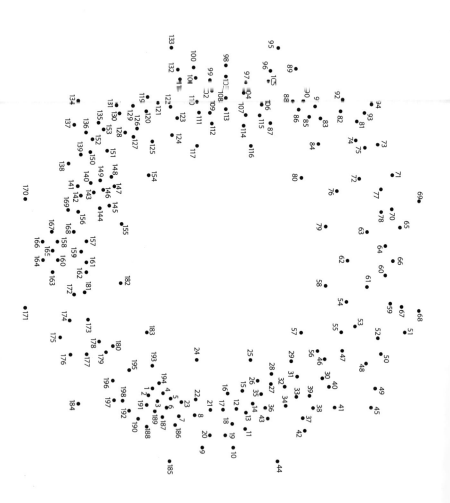

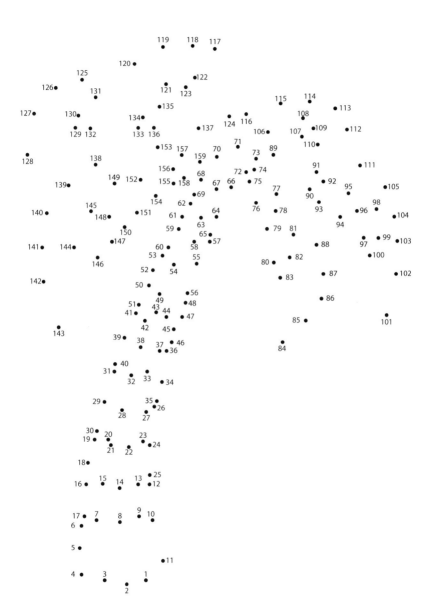

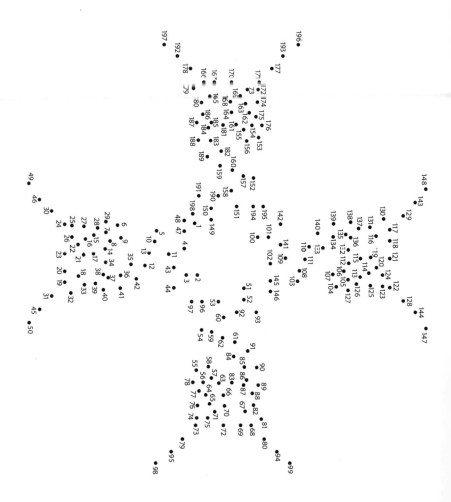

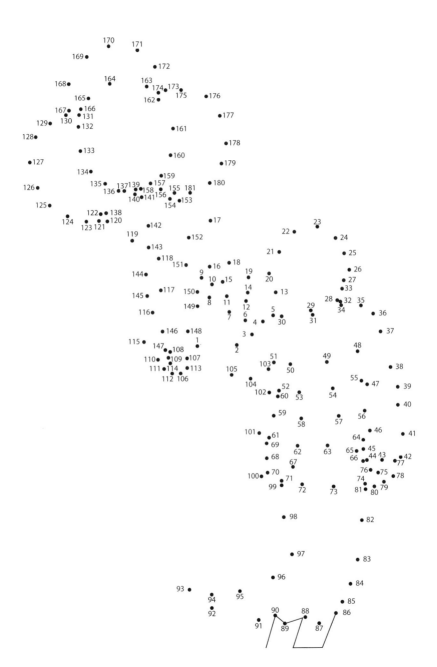

41

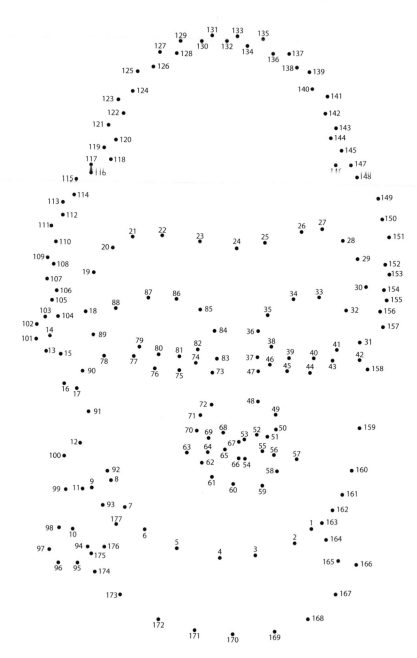

42

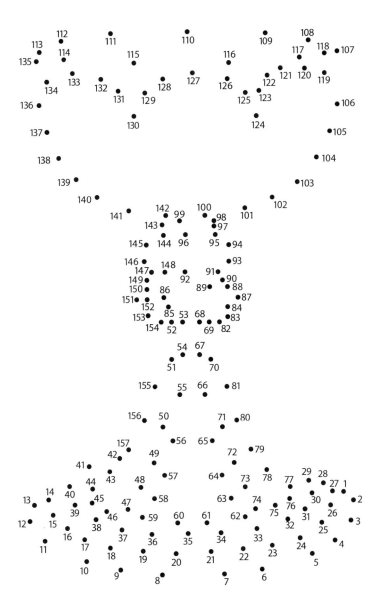

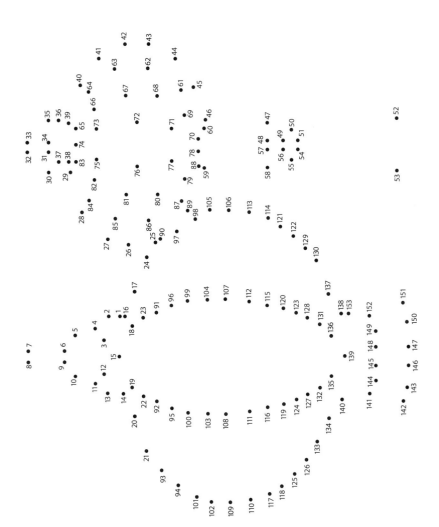

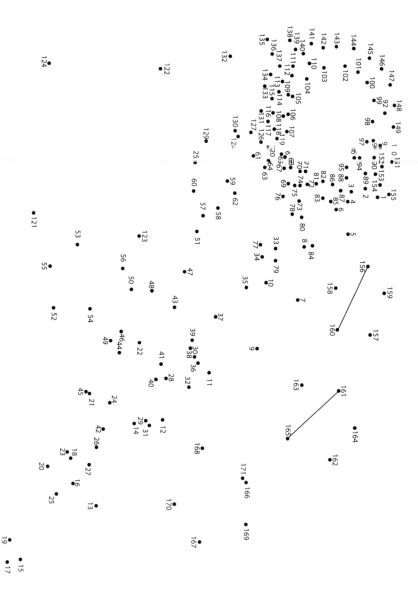

46

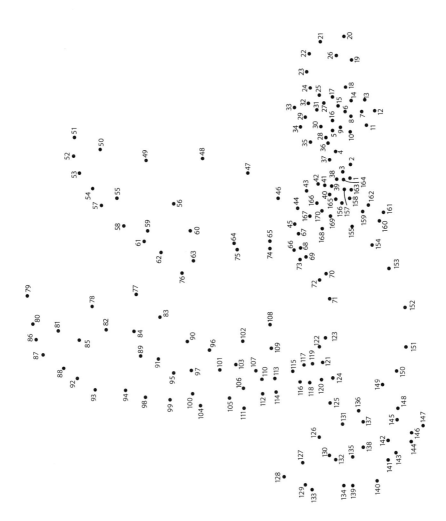

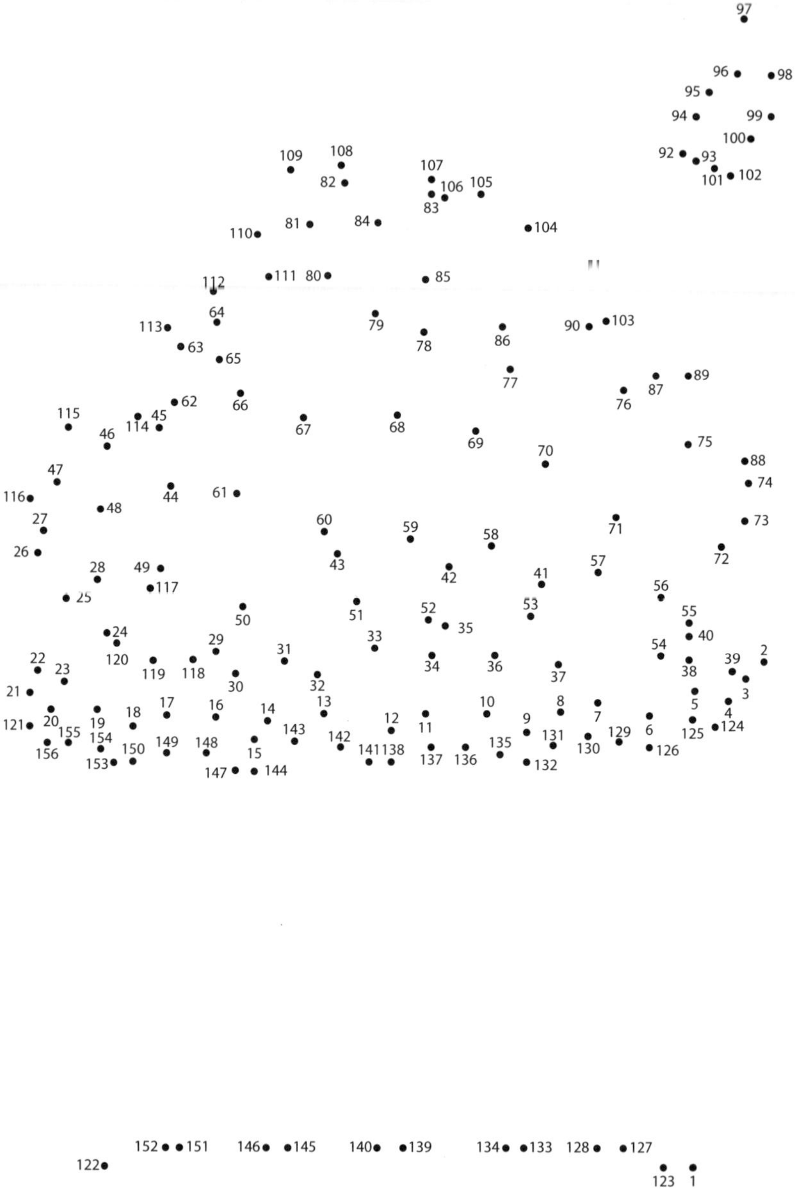

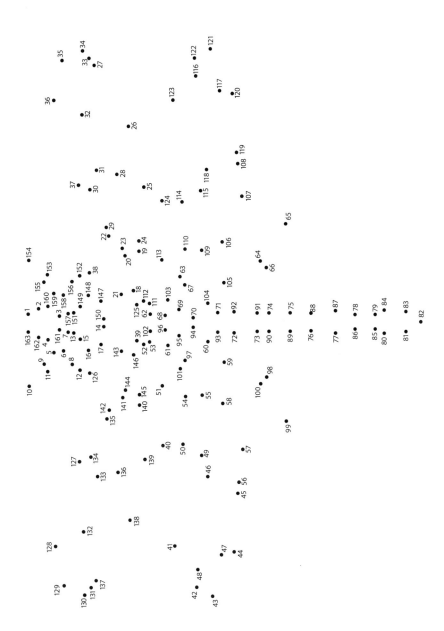

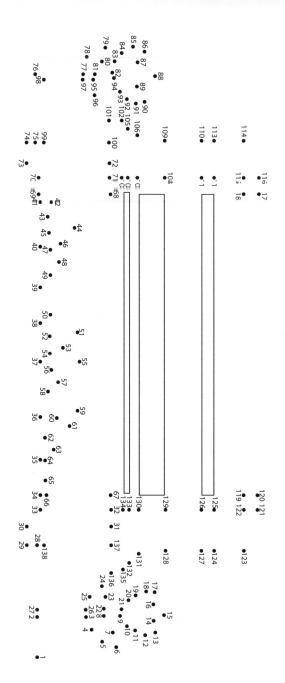

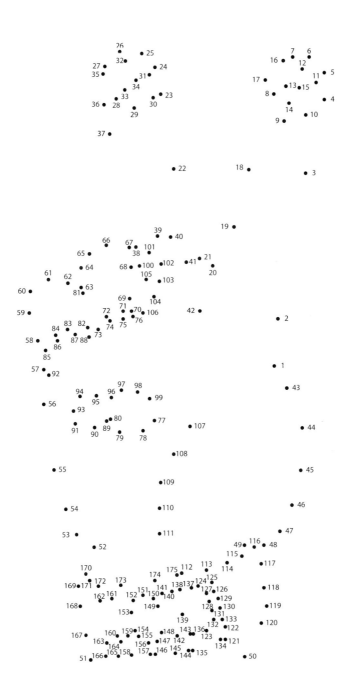

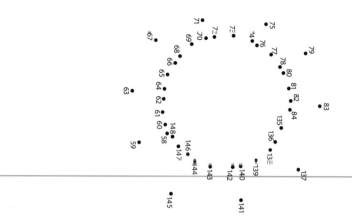

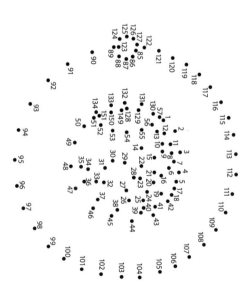

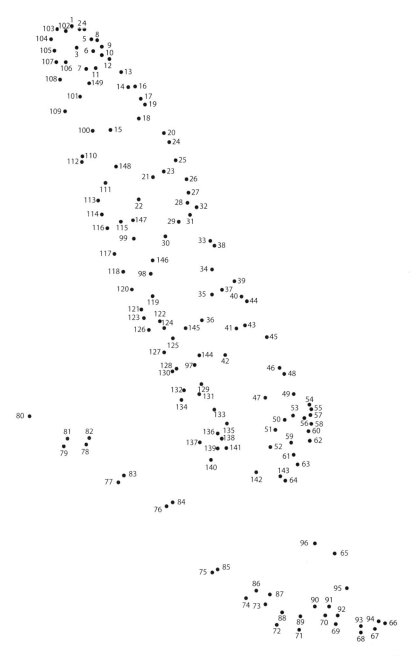

55

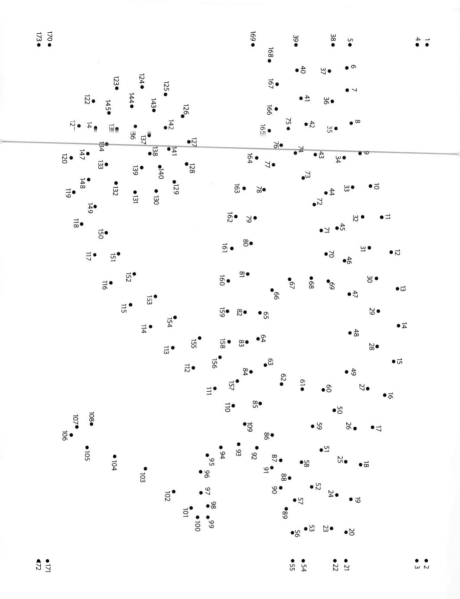

56

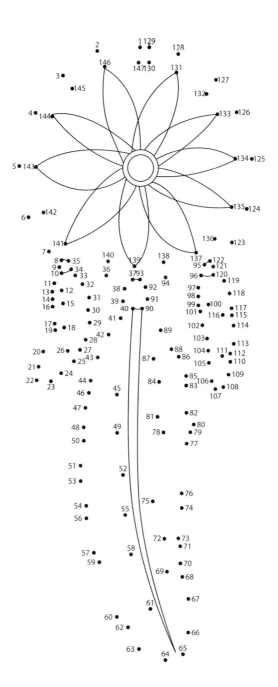

104

103 • 105
127

106 • 126
102 • 128
107 • 125
129

101 • 108 • 124
100 • 130
109 • 123
131

99 •
98 • 110 • 122 132

79 80 97 • 111 • 121 133

81 134
78 • 82
57 • 112 • 120 135
77 • 58 83
56 • 76 113 • 119
75 • 59 84 136
55 • 74 • 60 85 94 • 114 • 118
54 • 73 • 61 86 115 • 117 137
53 • 72 • 62 93 116
52 • 71 • 63 87 138 145 146
70 • 64 88 92
51 • 69 • 65 89 • 91 139 144 147
50 • 68 • 66 143 148
49 • 67 142 154 153 152 151
32 48 90 141 156 155 159 160 161 162 163 149
20 • 33 34 35 140 158 150 164
19 • 31 36 37 157 165
18 • 21 30 38 1 172
22 29 39 47 166
17 • 28 40 46 2 171
16 • 24 27 41 170 167
15 • 25 42 45 169 168
14 • 26
13 • 43
12 • 44
11 •
10 • 9 •
8 • 3
7 •
6 •
5 • 4

**59**

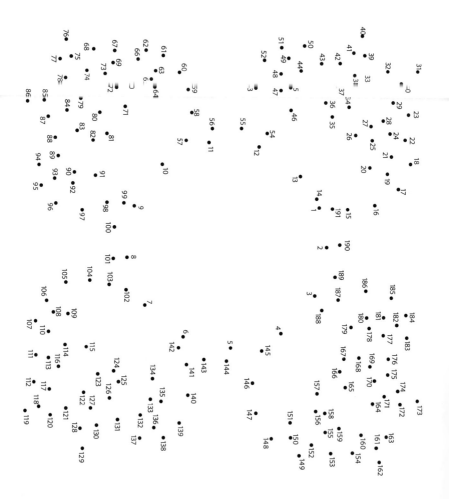

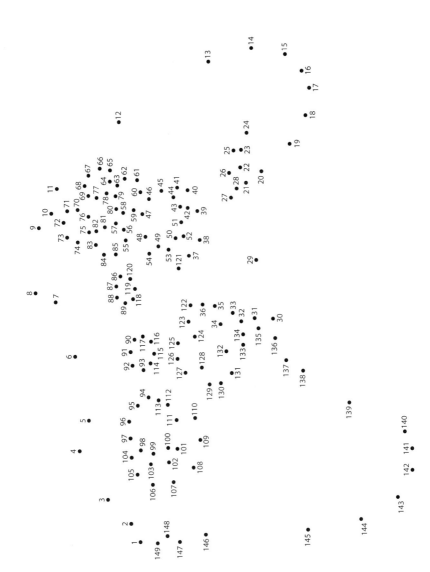

61

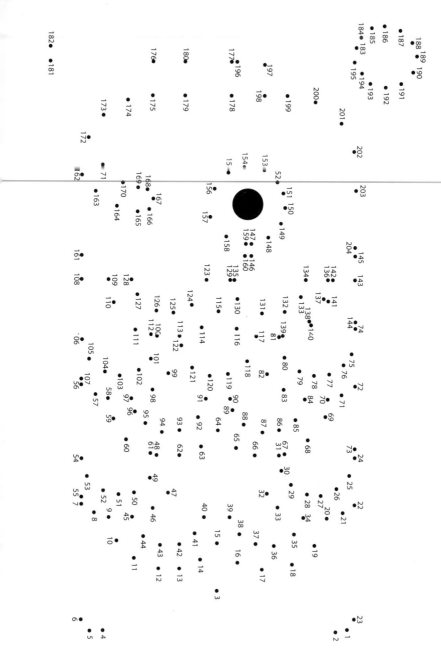

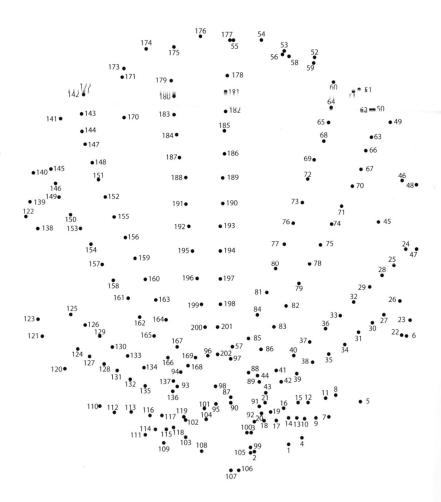

65

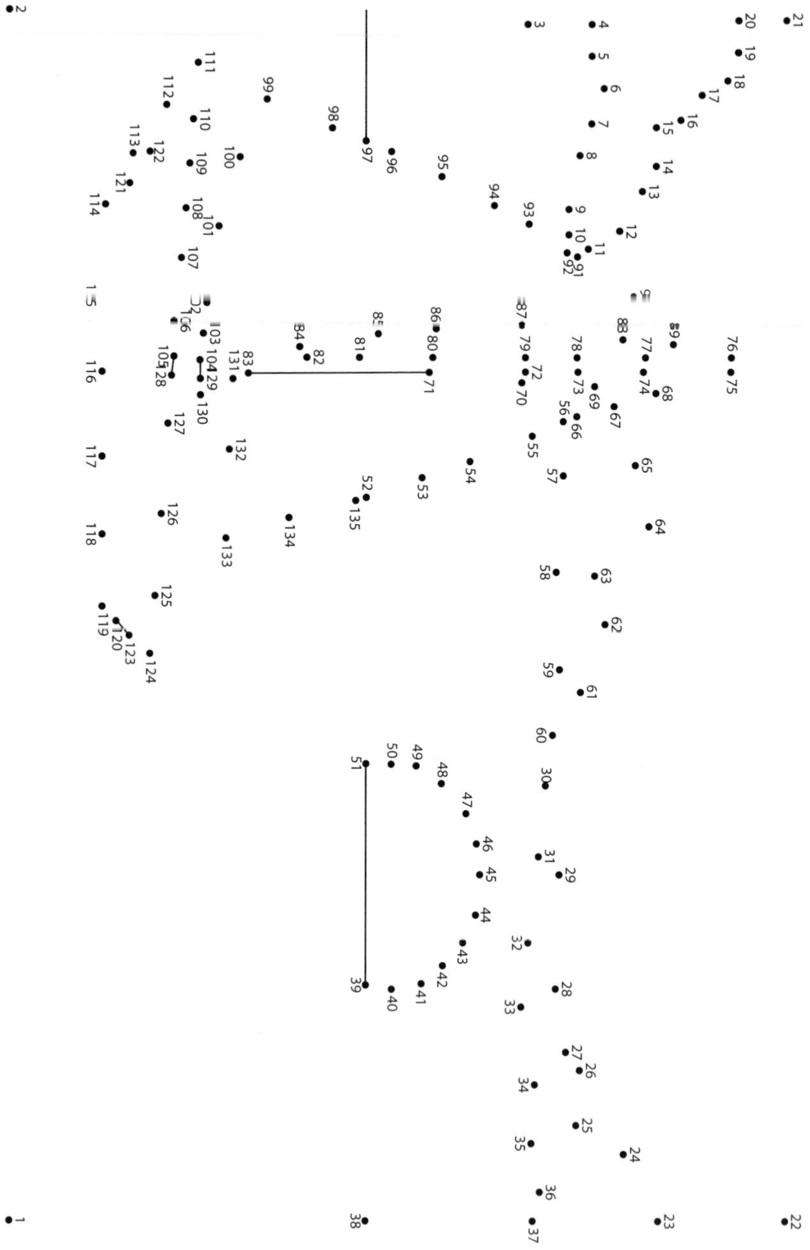

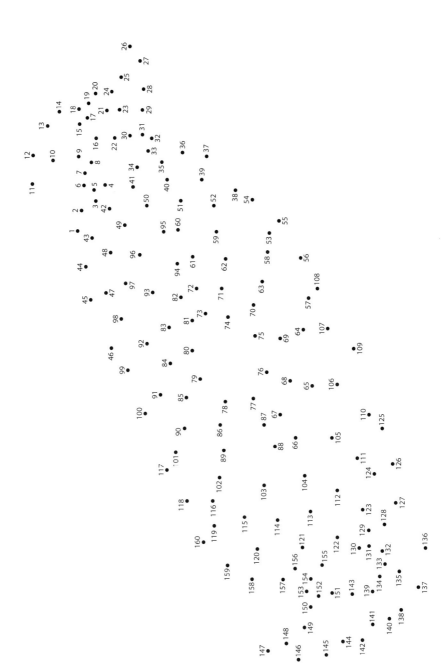

67

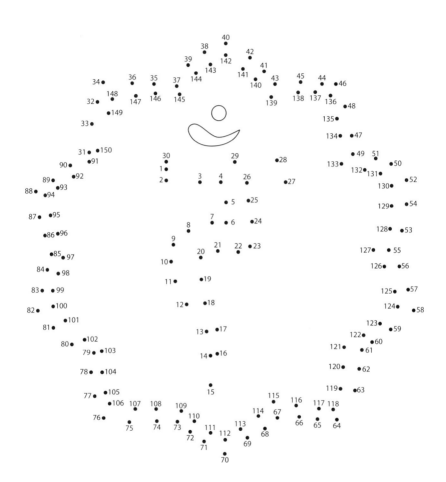

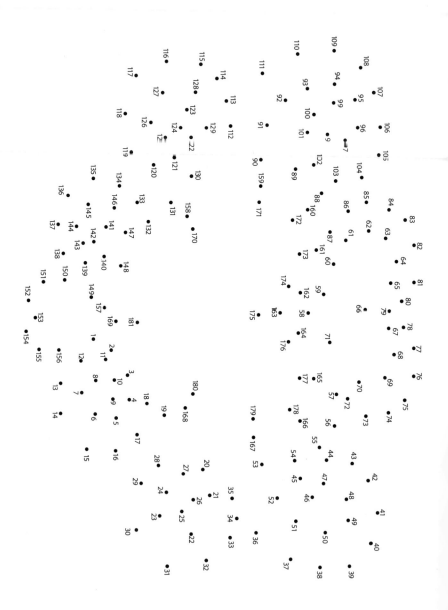

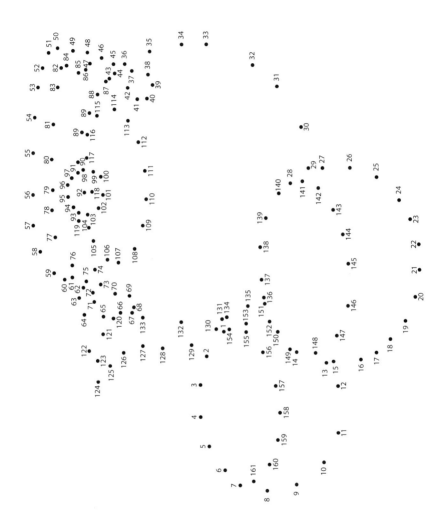

74

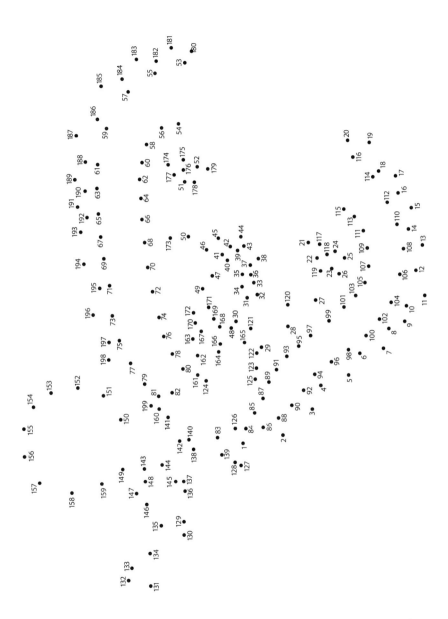

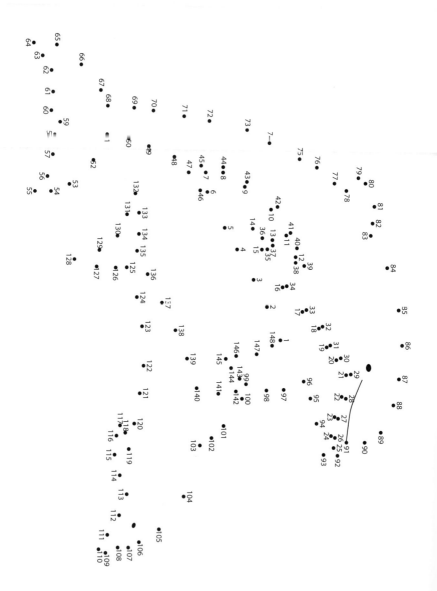

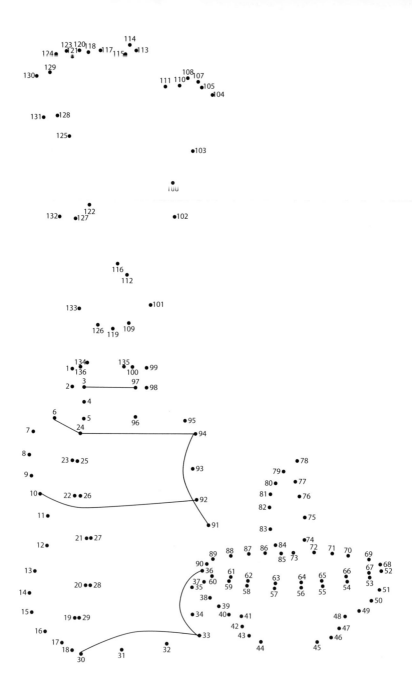

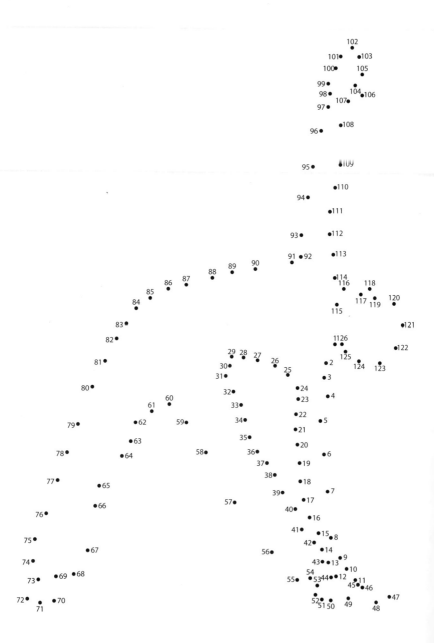

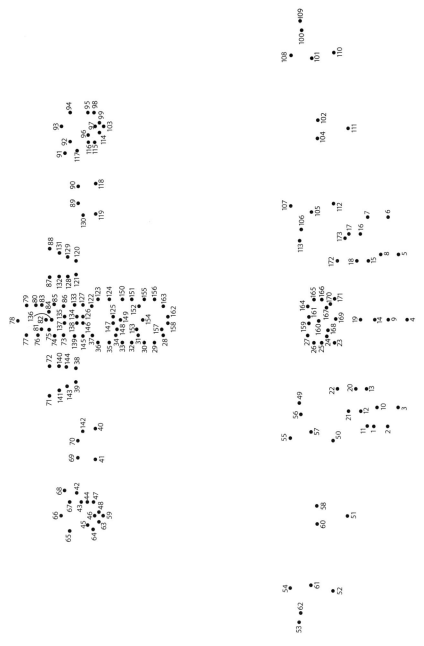

82

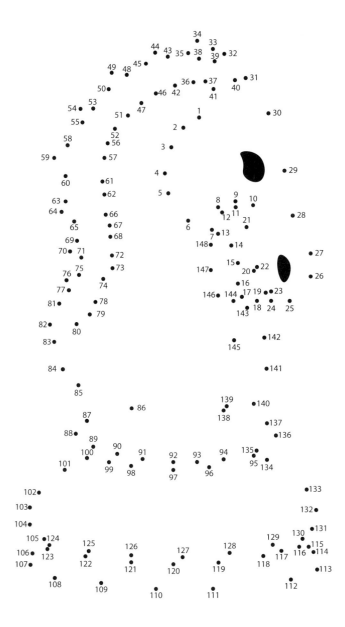

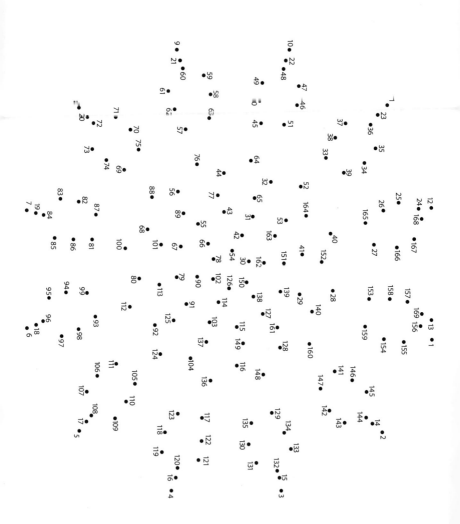

86

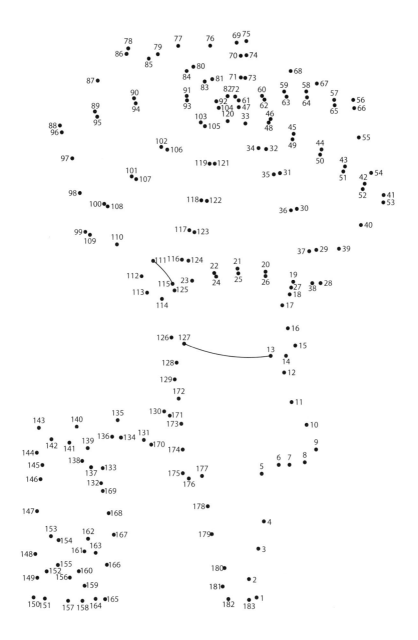

88

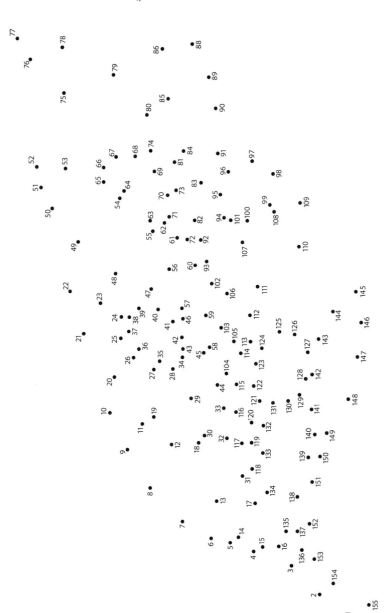

89

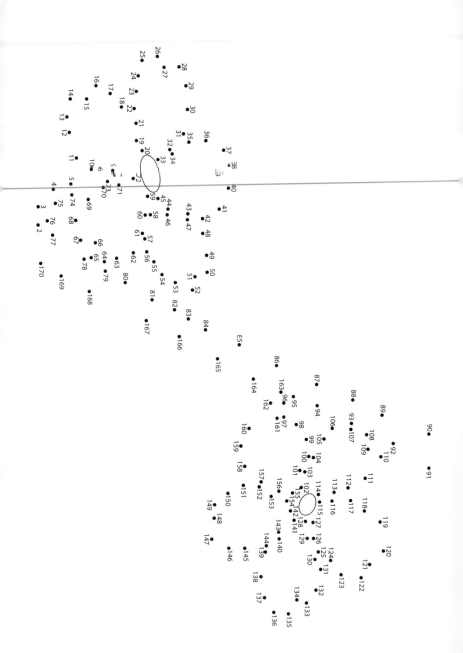

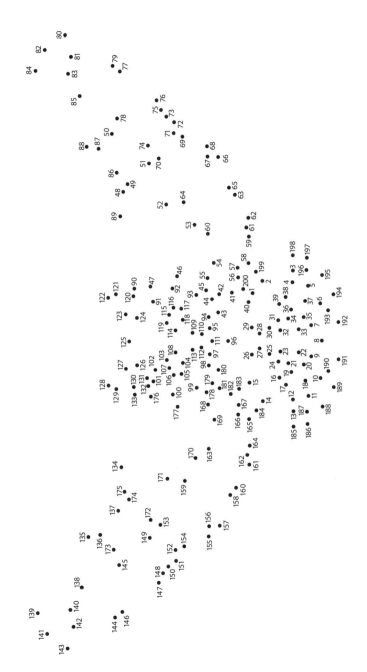

92

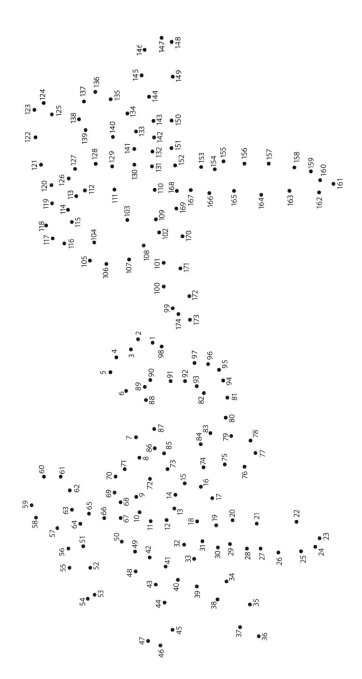

93

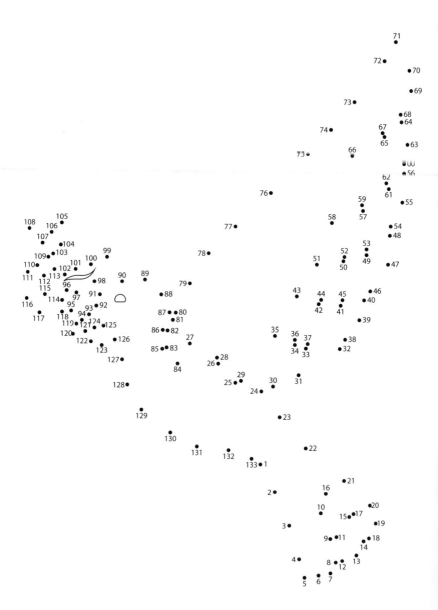

95

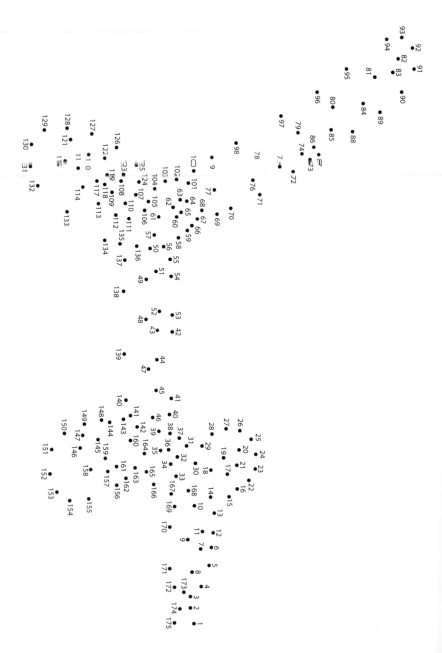

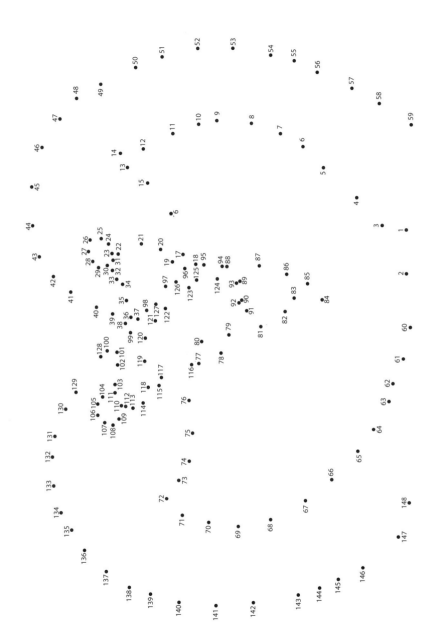

97

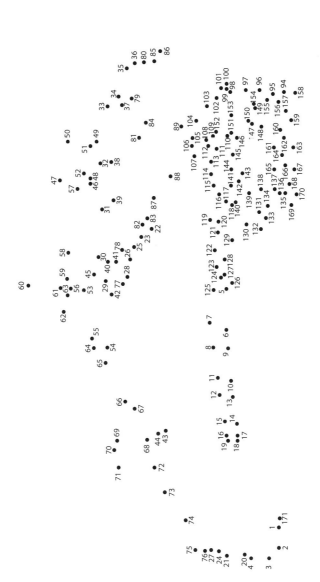

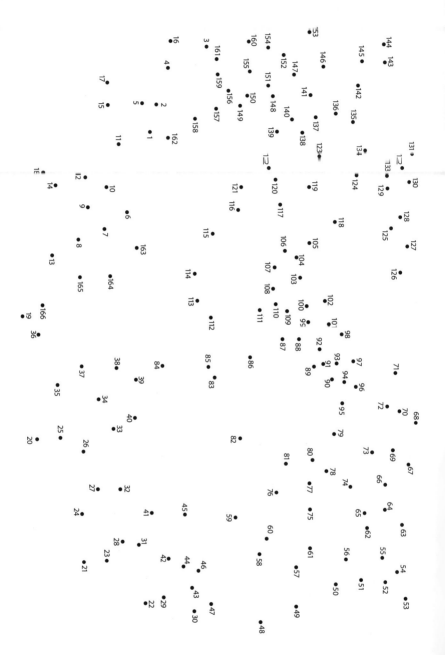

100

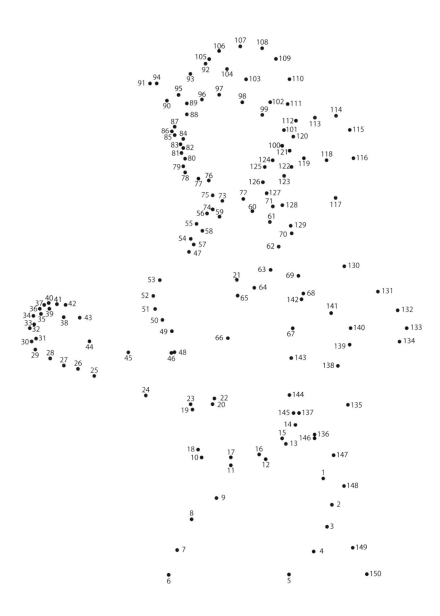

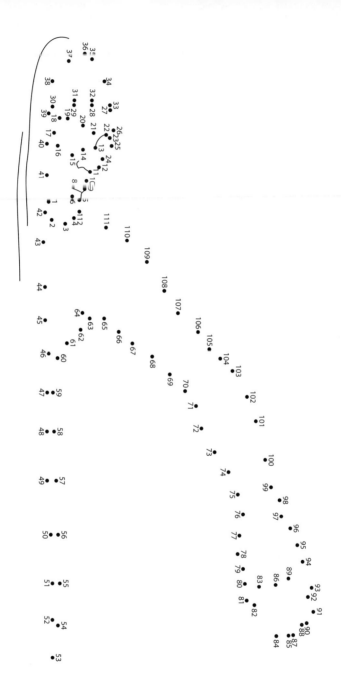

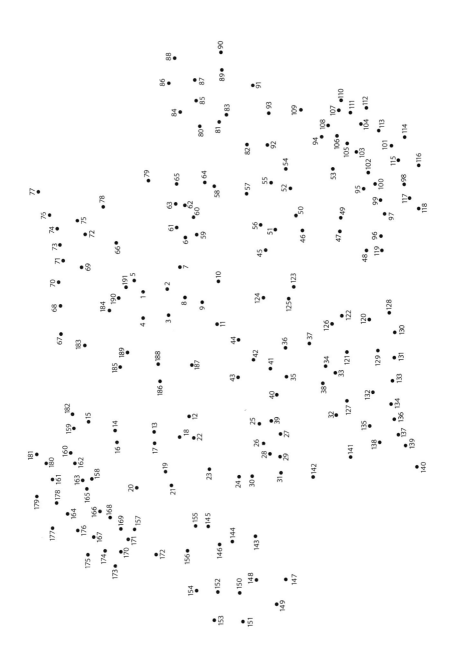

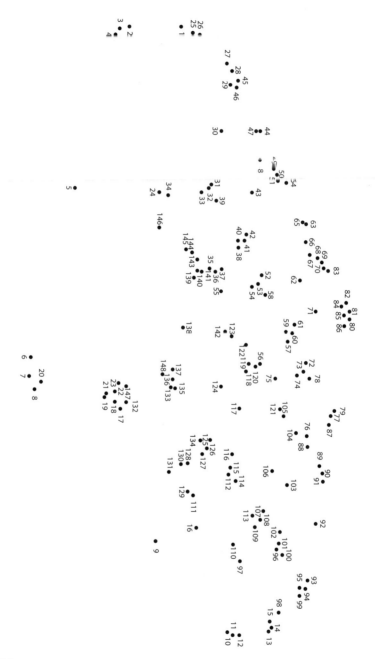

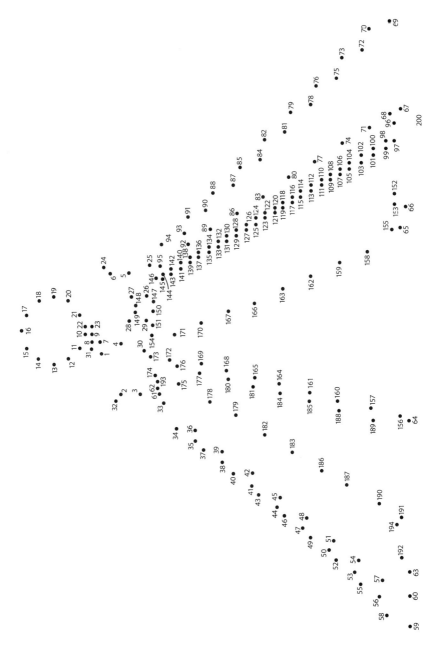

105

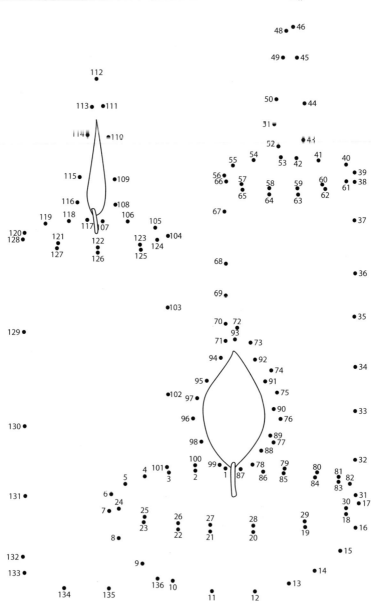

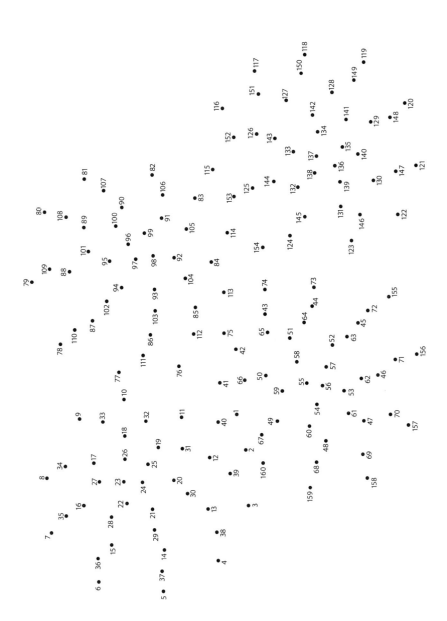

107

108

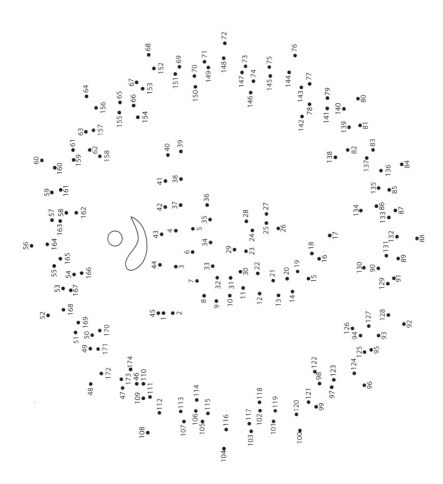

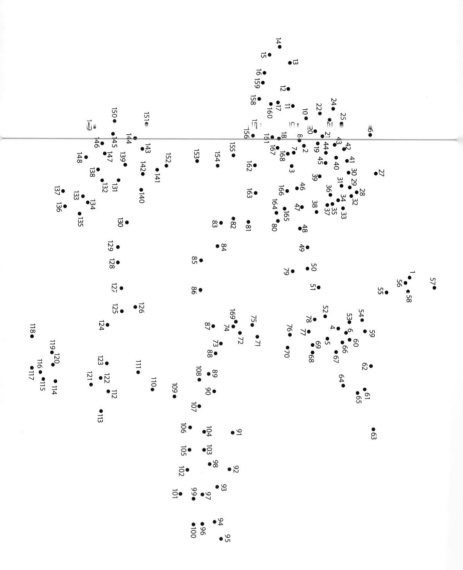

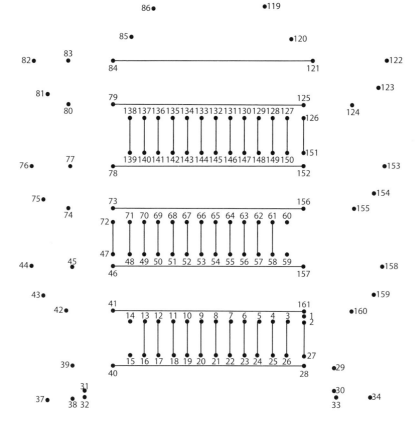

112

113

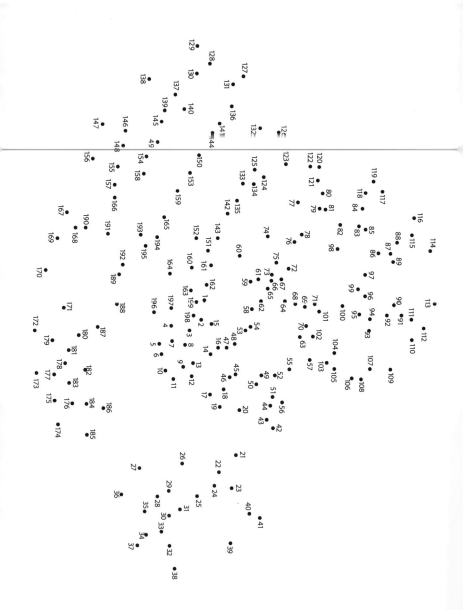

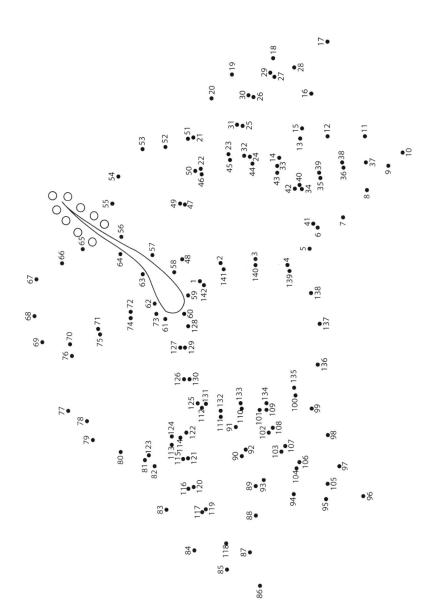

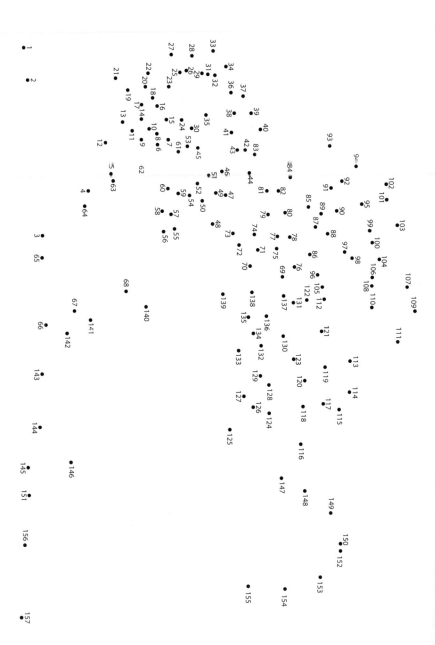

116

117

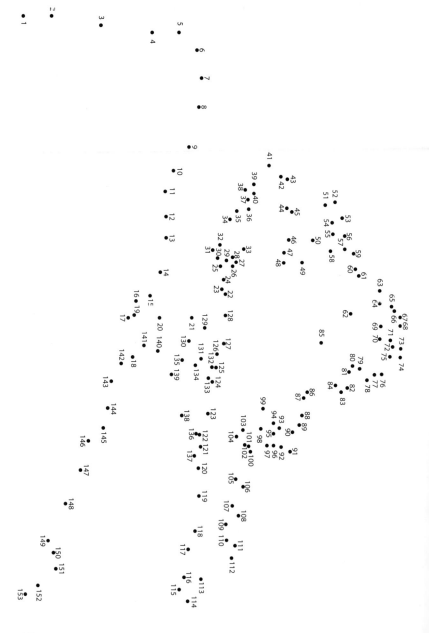

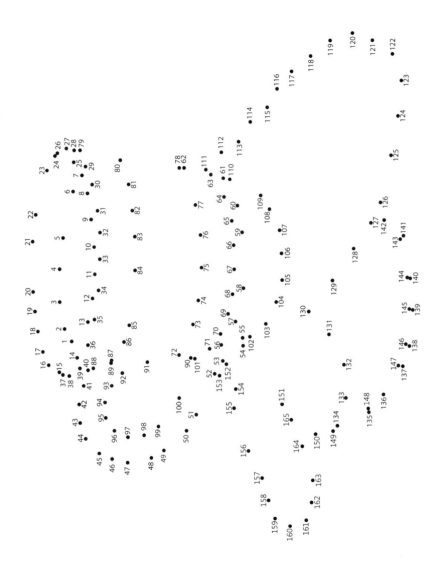

121

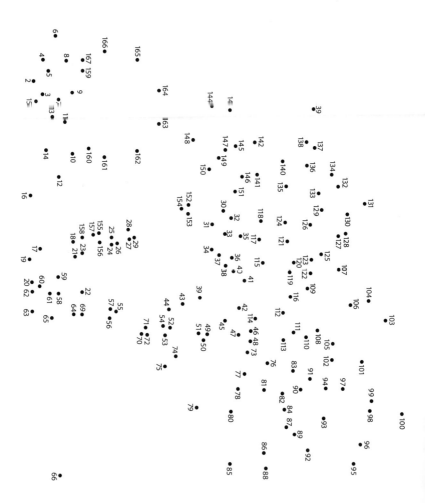

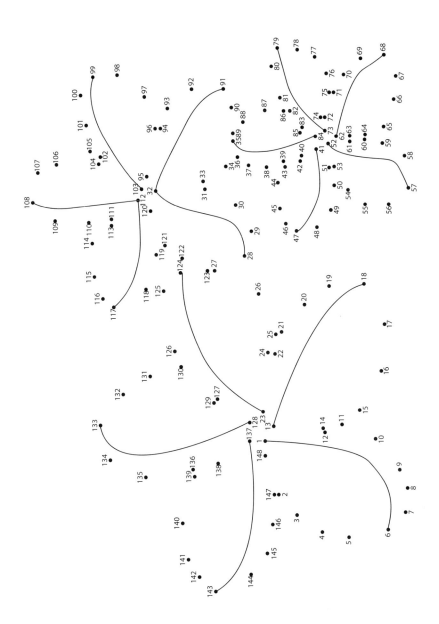

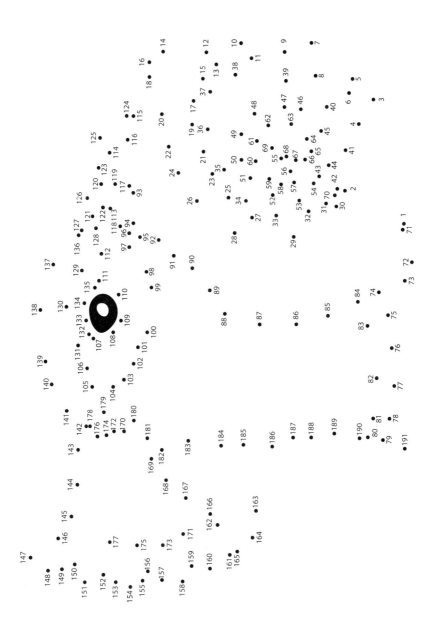

125

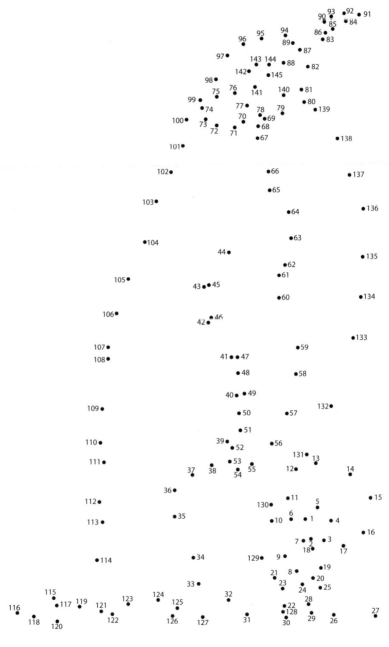

127

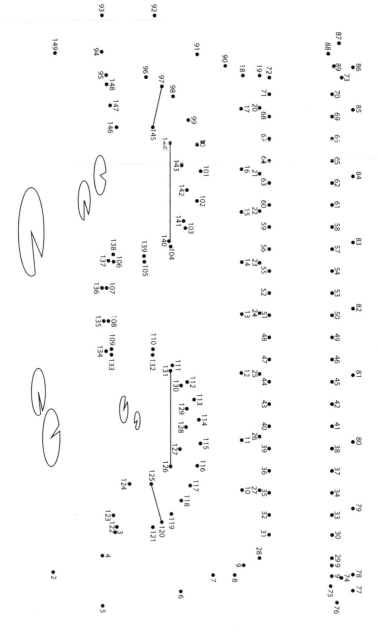

129

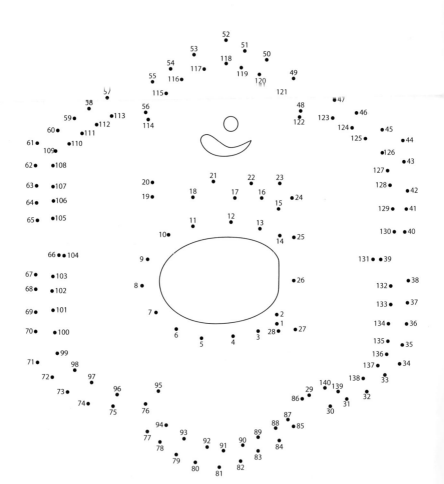

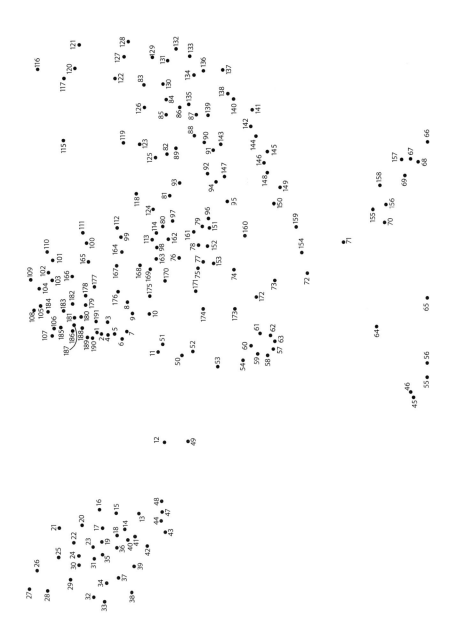

131

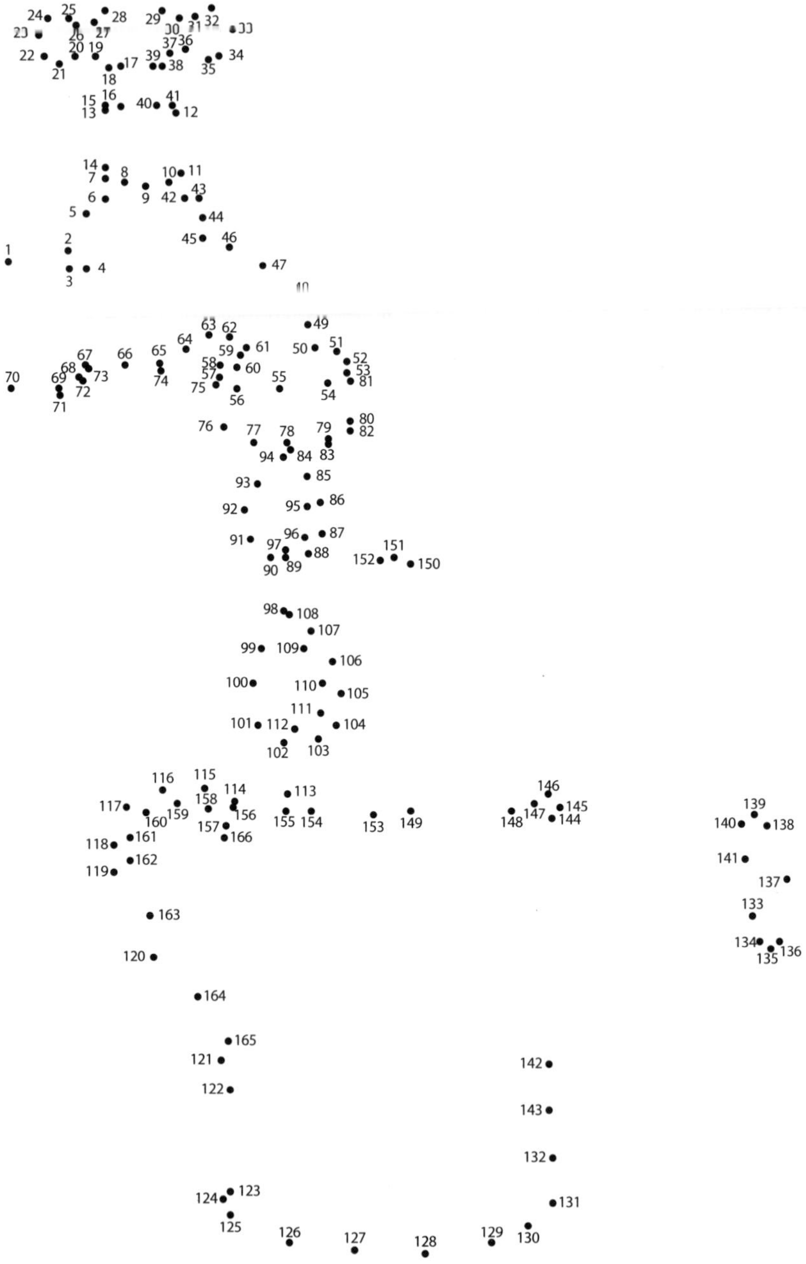

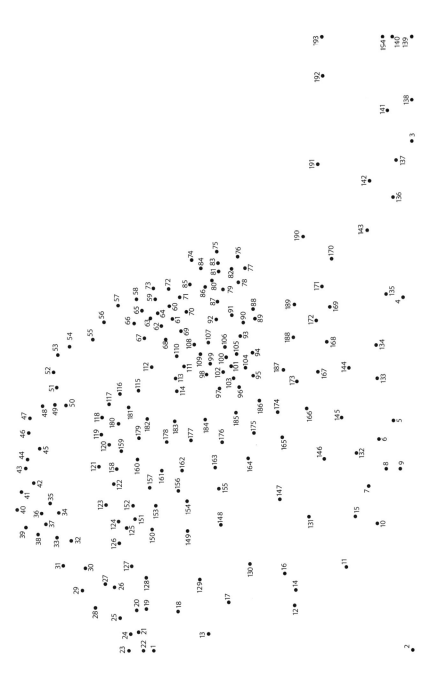

133

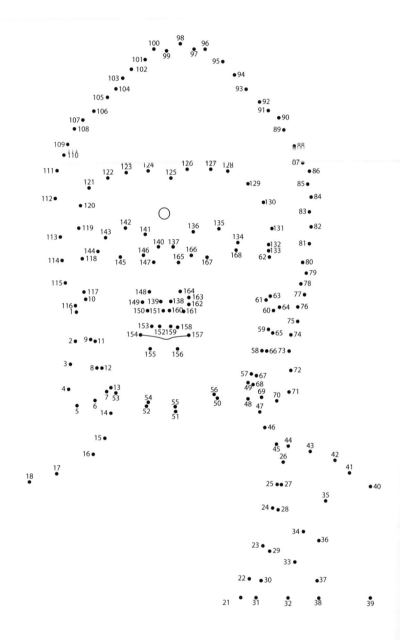

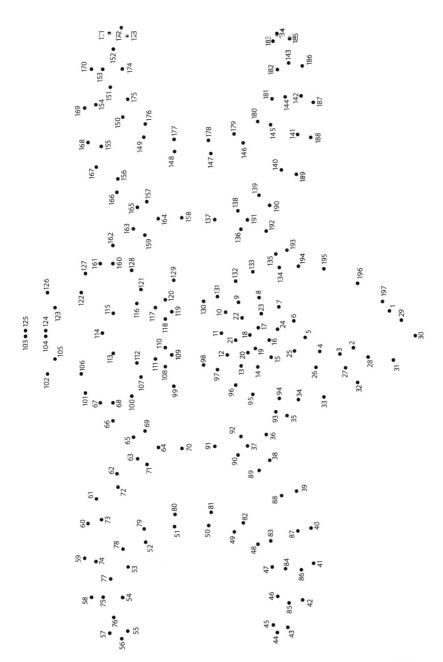

135

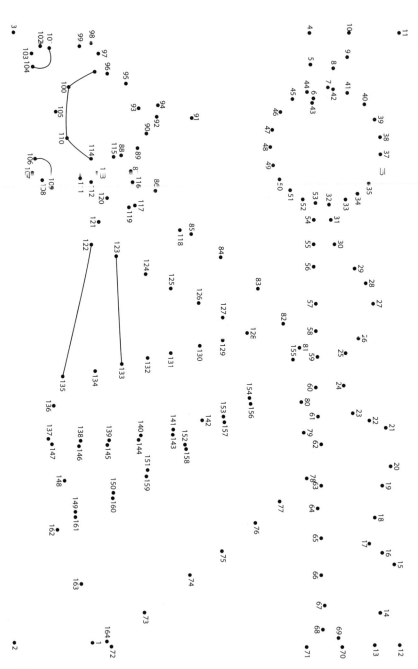

136

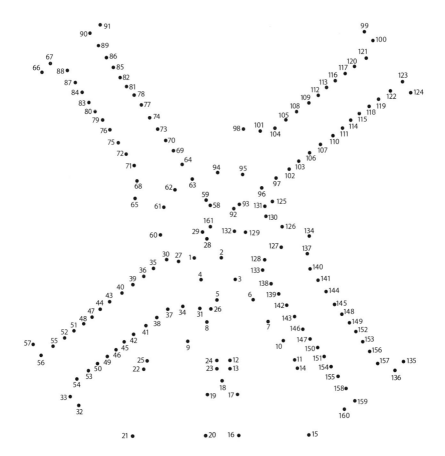

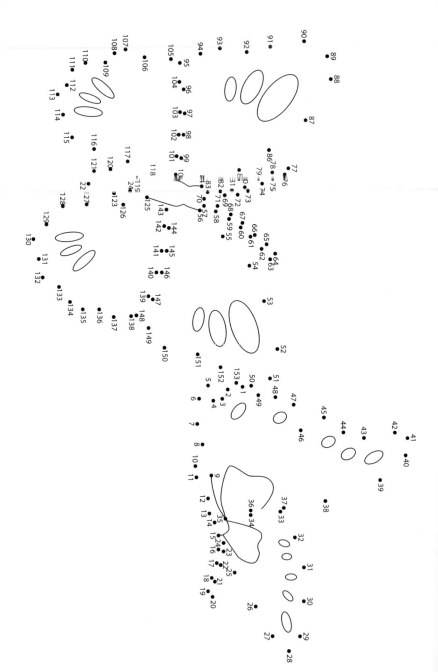

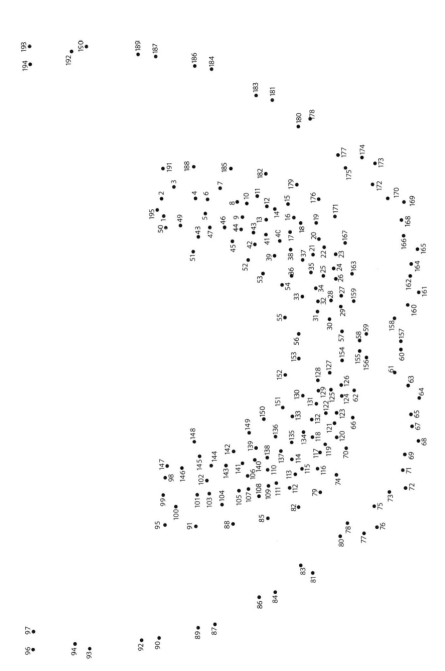

139

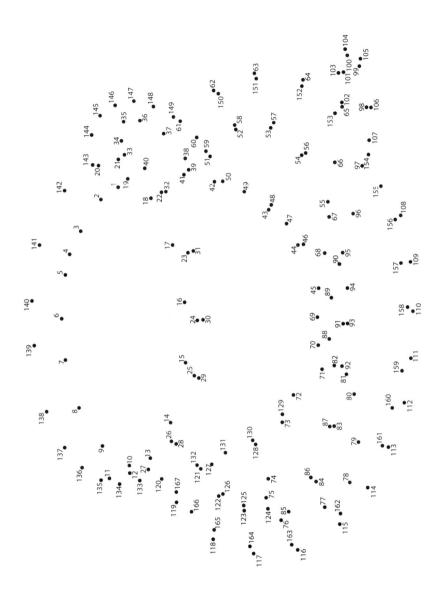

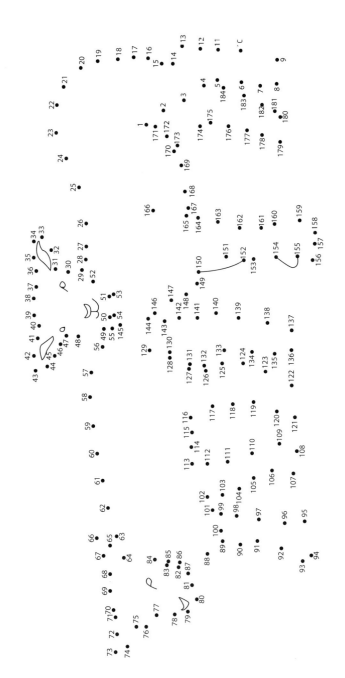

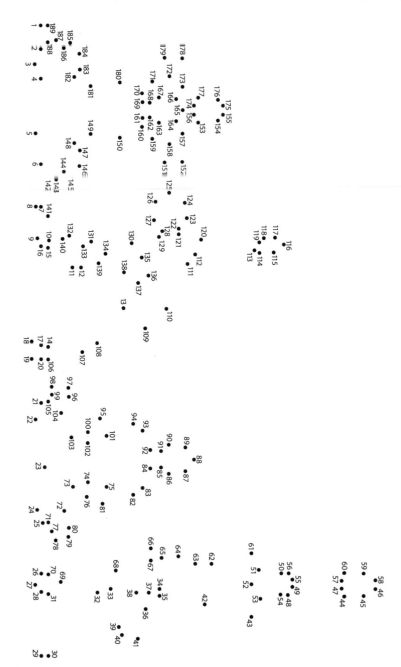

144

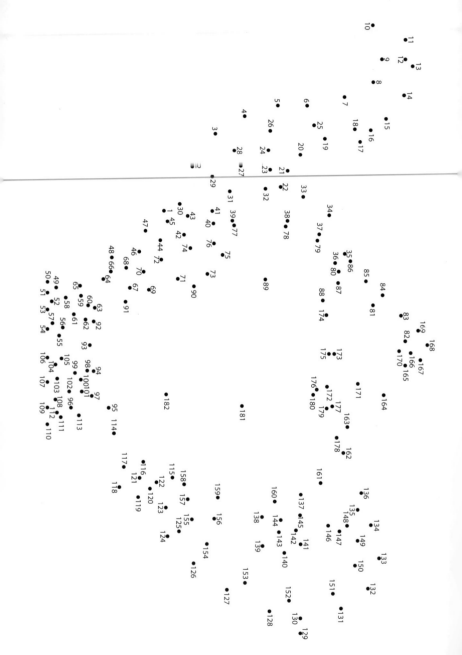

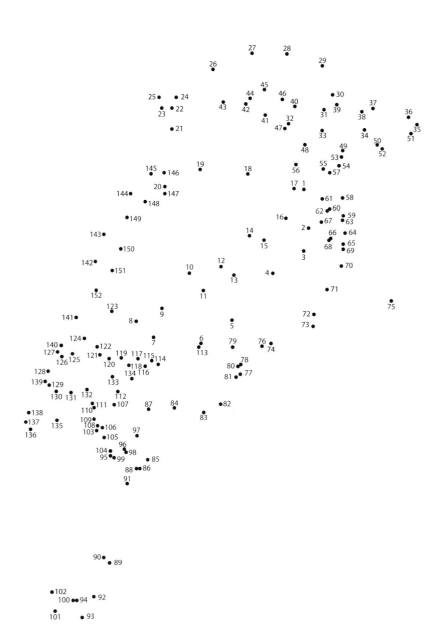

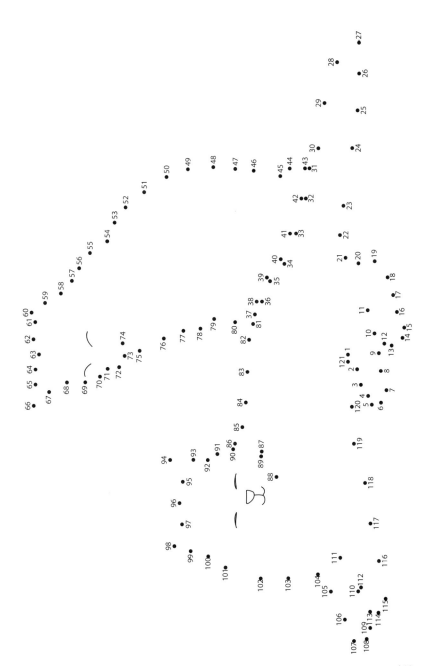

149

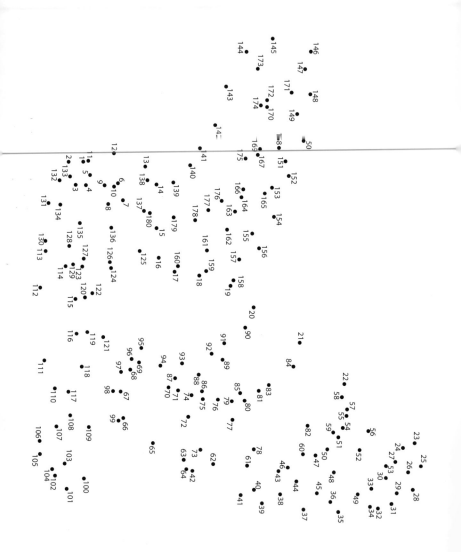

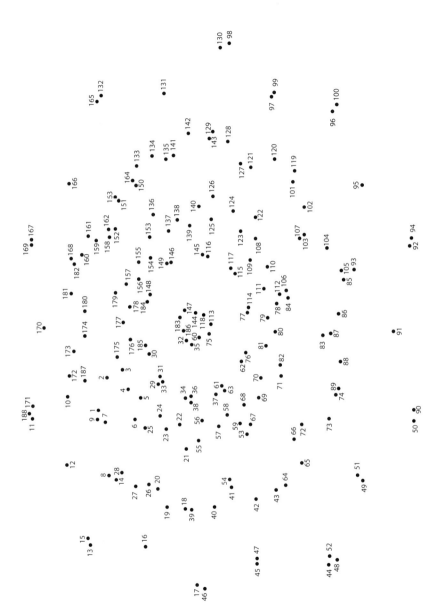

151

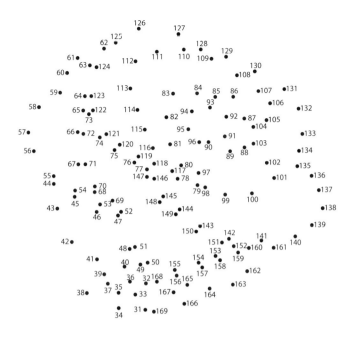

154

157

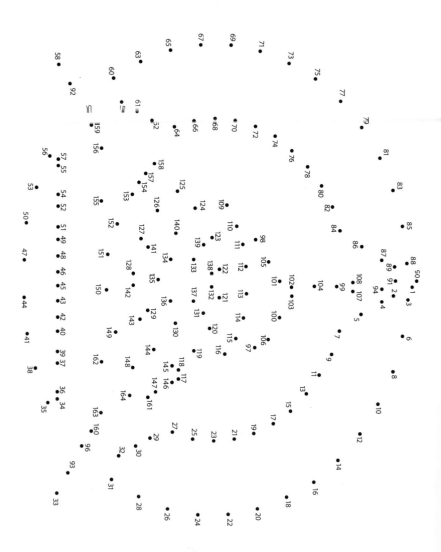

# List of illustrations